Little Boy Jesus

Written by Marti Beuschlein

Illustrated by Reg Sandland

CPH
Concordia Publishing House

Copyright © 1998 Concordia Publishing House
3558 S. Jefferson Avenue, St. Louis, MO 63118-3968
Manufactured in the United States of America

1   2   3   4   5   6   7   8   9   10   07 06 05 04 03 02 01 00 99 98

Stretch, stretch, stretch.
Little Boy Jesus wakes up.

Roll, roll, roll.
Jesus rolls up His blanket bed all by Himself.
He prays, "Thank You, God, for this day."

Walk, walk, walk.
Mary and Little Boy Jesus walk to the well
with friends.

Splash, splash, splash.
Little Boy Jesus dips the jar in the well.
He pulls up cool water to drink.

Help, help, help.
Mary says, "I need wood for the fire."

Work, work, work.
Pick up sticks. Gather wood.
Little Boy Jesus likes helping His mother.

Grind, grind, grind.
Little Boy Jesus helps Mary grind flour for
bread.

Bang, bang, bang.
Little Boy Jesus will also help Joseph.
Jesus will help pound nails.

Talk, talk, talk.
Little Boy Jesus likes to go to school.
He likes to hear about God's love.

Run, run, run.
Soon Little Boy Jesus will run and play
with His friends.

Yum, yum, yum.
Little Boy Jesus eats bread and dates
and melon and cucumbers.

Read, read, read.
Now Joseph will read God's Word from the scroll.
The words say, "God loves you!"

Look, look, look.
What a pretty night!
The moon and stars are shining.

Yawn, yawn, yawn.
Time for bed, Little Boy Jesus.

Sleep, sleep, sleep.
Good night, Little Boy Jesus.
Mary and Joseph say,
"God will watch over You."